Gar

Shove At
First Sight

JiM DAViS

© 1998 PAWS INCORPORATED
(www.garfield.com)

All rights reserved

First published by Ravette Publishing 1998

Printed and bound in Great Britain
for Ravette Publishing Limited,
Unit 3, Tristar Centre,
Star Road, Partridge Green,
West Sussex RH13 8RA
by Cox & Wyman Ltd, Reading, Berkshire

ISBN 1 85304 990 5

© 1995 PAWS, INC./Distributed by Universal Press Syndicate

© 1995 PAWS, INC./Distributed by Universal Press Syndicate

© 1995 PAWS, INC./Distributed by Universal Press Syndicate

© 1996 PAWS, INC./Distributed by Universal Press Syndicate

© 1995 PAWS, INC./Distributed by Universal Press Syndicate

© 1995 PAWS, INC./Distributed by Universal Press Syndicate

FWEEEEEEP

GARFIELD! NEW YEAR'S EVE ISN'T FOR THREE DAYS YET!

PRACTICE MAKES PERFECT

JIM DAVIS 12-8

JIM DAVIS 12-2

© 1995 PAWS, INC./Distributed by Universal Press Syndicate

© 1996 PAWS, INC./Distributed by Universal Press Syndicate

SIP

WHOA! GIVE **ME** SOME OF THAT!

JIM DAVIS 11-21

© 1996 PAWS, INC./Distributed by Universal Press Syndicate

TAP
TAP

JIM DAVIS 2-8

© 1996 PAWS, INC./Distributed by Universal Press Syndicate

OTHER GARFIELD BOOKS AVAILABLE

Classics @ £4.99 each   ISBN
Volume One   1 85304 970 0
Volume Two   1 85304 971 9

Miscellaneous
Garfield Treasury   £9.99   1 85304 975 1

Garfield Address & Birthday   1 85304 918 2
Book Gift Set   £7.99 inc VAT

All Garfield books are available at your local bookshop or from
the address below. Just tick the titles required and send the form
with your remittance to:-

  B.B.C.S., P.O. BOX 941, HULL, NORTH HUMBERSIDE HU1 3YQ
     24 Hour Telephone Credit Card Line 01482 224626
  Prices and availability are subject to change without notice.

Please enclose a cheque or postal order made payable to B.B.C.S.
to the value of the cover price of the book and allow the following
for postage and packing:

U.K. & B.F.P.O.:	£1.00 for the first book and 50p for each additional book to a maximum of £3.50.
Overseas & Eire	£2.00 for the first book, £1.00 for the second and 50p for each additional book.

                          BLOCK CAPITALS PLEASE

Name . . . .

Address. . . . .

. . . .

. . . .

Cards accepted: Mastercard and Visa

Expiry Date . . . . .Signature . . . .